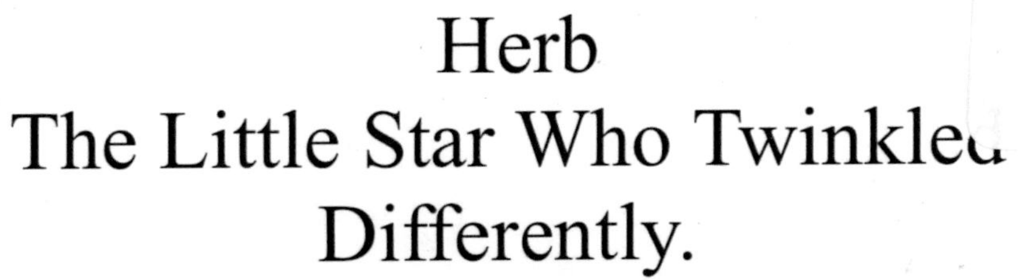

Herb
The Little Star Who Twinkled Differently.

Author G.L.Stone
Illustrator Elina Oplakanska

Herb
The Little Star Who Twinkled Differently.

Lovingly dedicated to every Herb
shining brightly, and those who love
them dearly.

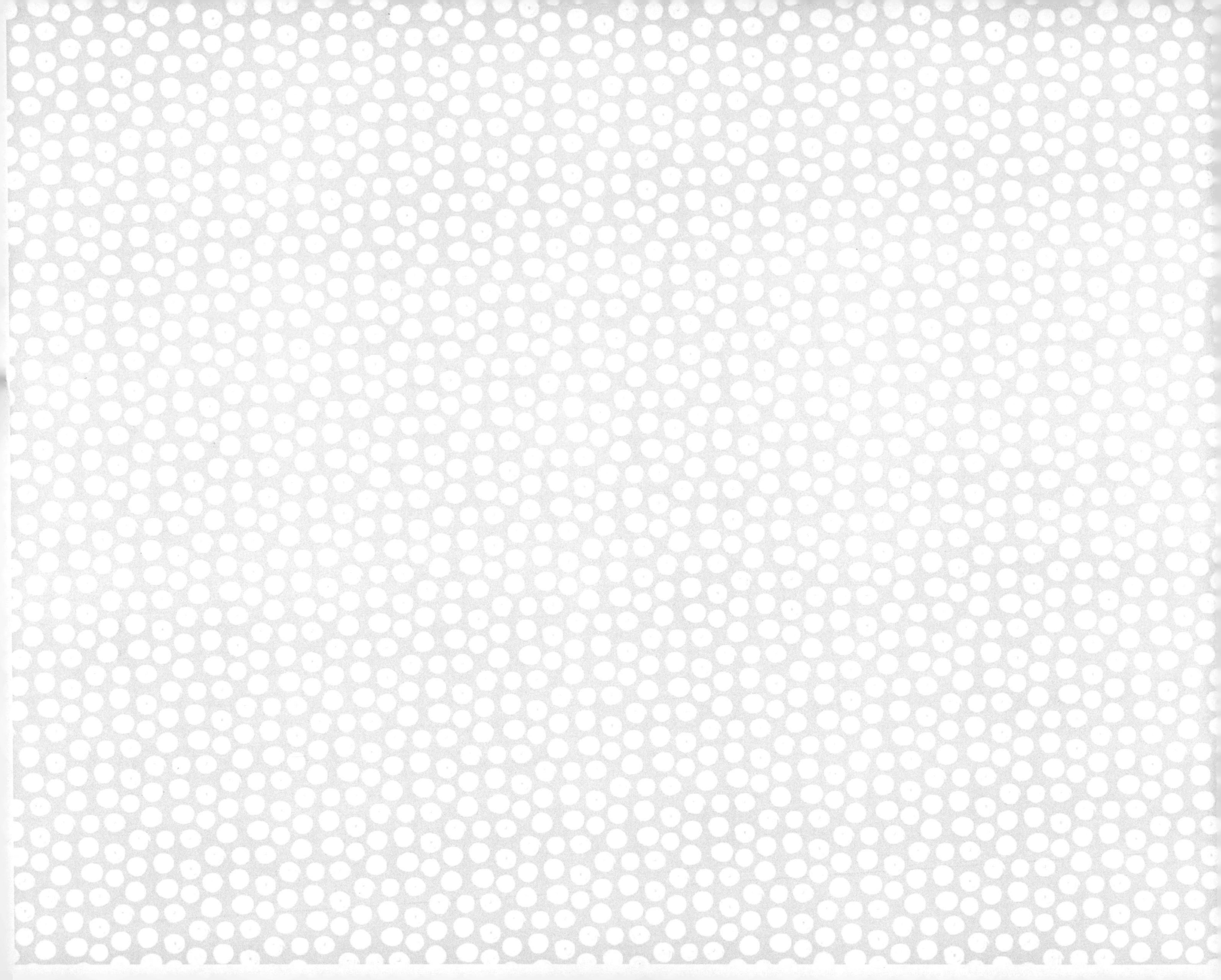

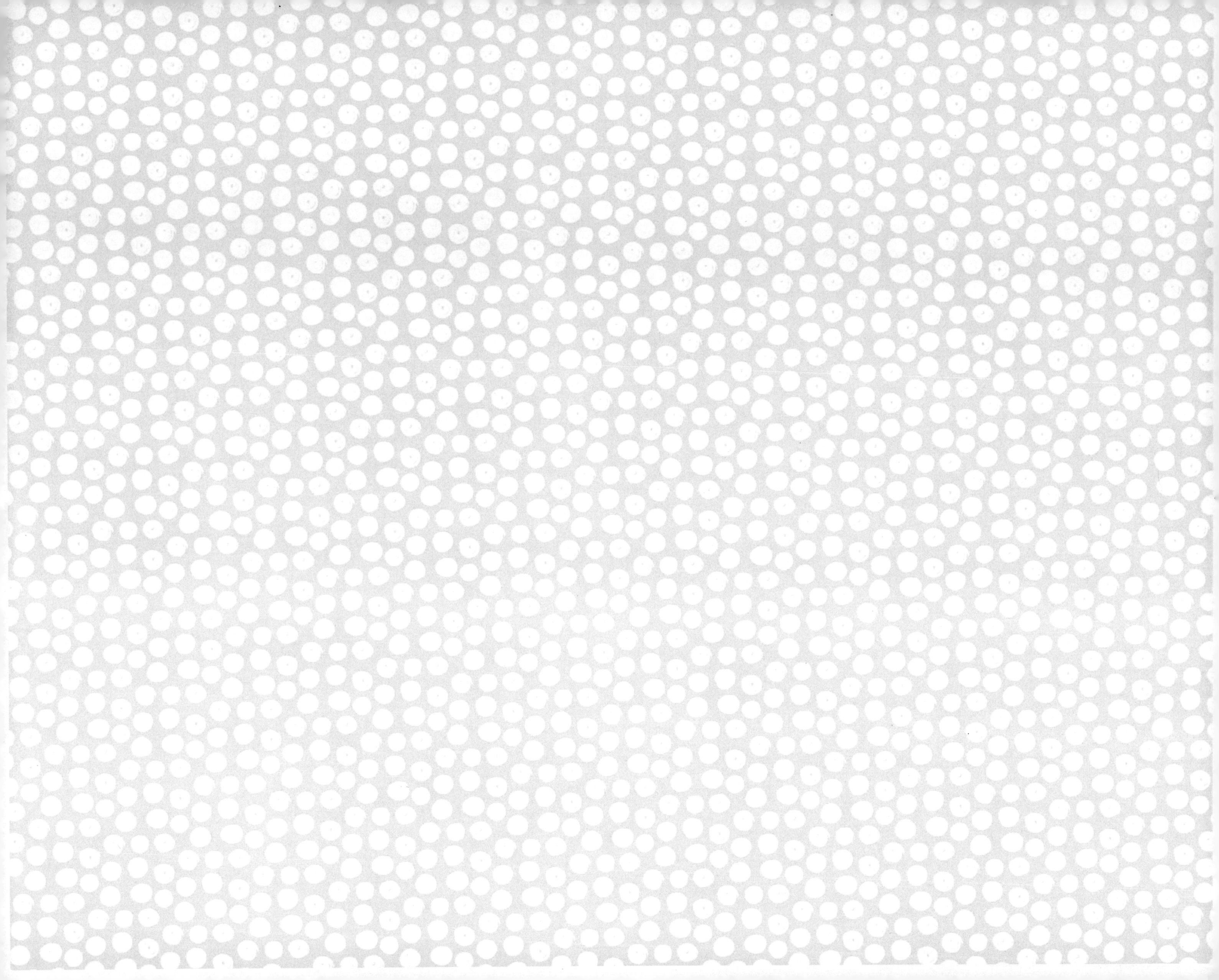

This is Herb.

His favourite things to do are:
1. Twinkle
2. Twirl
3. And swoosh
In no particular order.

One starry night when Herb was doing
what Herb does best,
he noticed something
he had not noticed before.

Herb looked very closely.. Yup, he was certain.
One of his five points was much shorter than his others.

Feeling a little worried, Herb tried to stretch it out a little further…
'mmmmmeemmmmm' nothing?
So he tried again…
And again…
And again. But stretching was impossible.

'How peculiar?' he muttered to himself.
With a shrug, Herb carried on getting ready to do what Herb does best when he noticed something he had not noticed before… All of his friends had five even-length points.. He was the only one with a short one.

Slowly Herb's bright twinkle started to dim.

He didn't feel like twinkling or twirling… not even swooshing. He didn't want to be seen doing what Herb does best.

Herb floated quietly, gazing at his different, shorter point.
'Why are you different?' He whispered. 'Has anyone else noticed you?'

When a star that shines as bright as Herb dims a little, it can be seen for miles around. So, unsurprisingly, it didn't take long for those who loved him to worry.
'Is everything okay?' asked Herb's Dad worryingly.

Herb thought hard for a moment. Finding the right words to say felt a little trickier than it usually did.

With no response, Herb just gave his shorter point a little wiggle.

Dad floated in a little closer.
'Can I ask, did you twinkle any less yesterday or twirl any slower? Was your swooshing anything other than spectacular?' he asked.

Herb thought hard.

'I remember a little star who used to find the things he does best now, the hardest things to do then' smiled Dad.'But he never gave up on himself. And now.. now he is the brightest star in the constellation.'

Herb twinkled. 'Thank you, Dad', he said, giving him the biggest squish before rushing off to make up for lost time doing what Herb does best.

Herb took a deep breath. Allowing himself to be seen (and seen for his difference) felt scary, but he knew just how bright he could and was going to shine.

'Ready?' Herb whispered to himself

SWOOOOOOOOOOOOSSSSSH

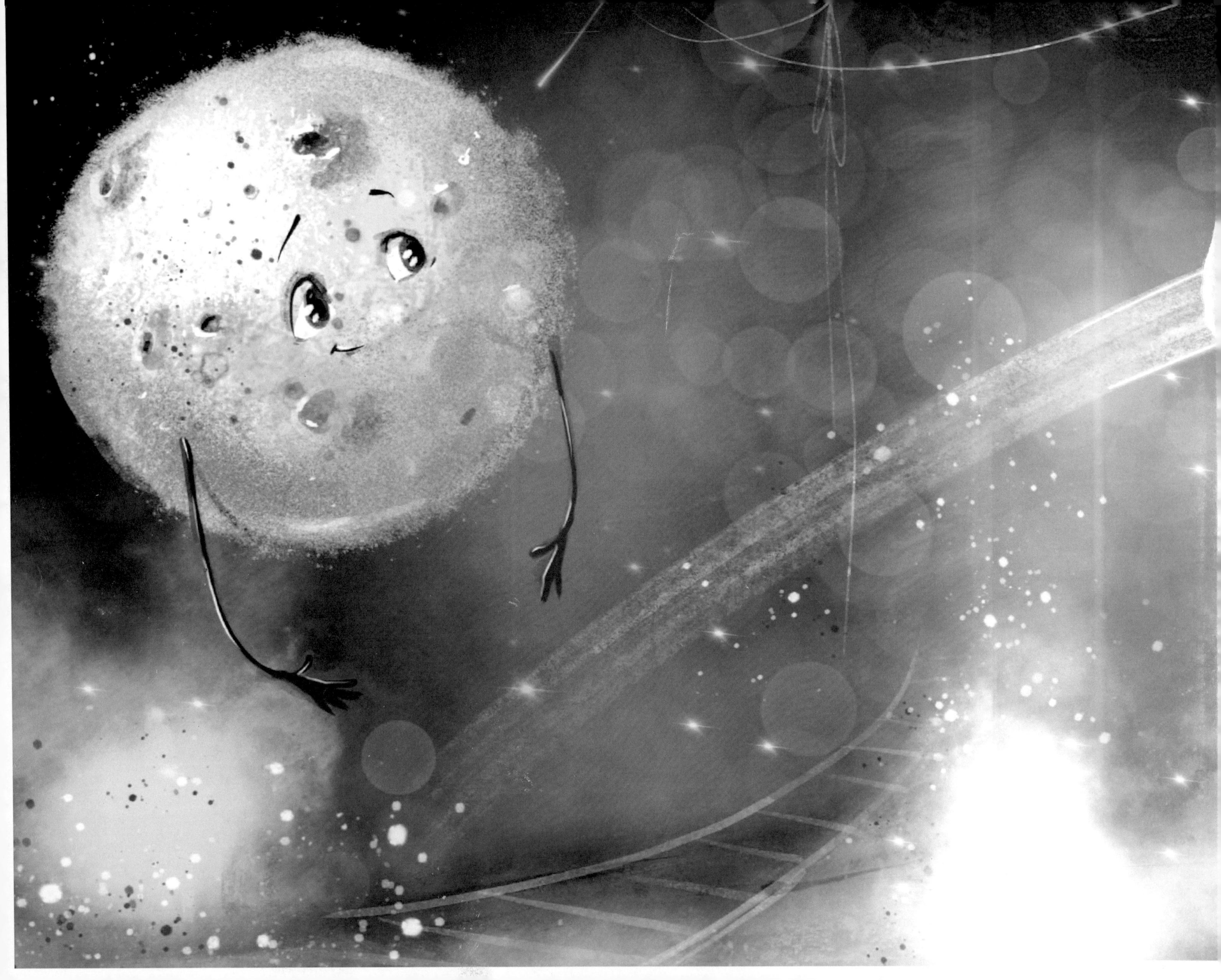

Lightning Source UK Ltd.
Milton Keynes UK
UKRC032107140922
408854UK00001B/1

* 9 7 8 1 3 9 9 9 2 5 0 7 5 *